50 MELODY LINE ARRANGEMENTS +
50 mp3 BACKING TRACKS +
50 mp3 DEMO TRACKS!*

PLAYALONG 50/50
FLUTE
50 POP HITS

Published by
WISE PUBLICATIONS
14-15 Berners Street, London W1T 3LJ,
United Kingdom.

Exclusive Distributors:
MUSIC SALES LIMITED
Distribution Centre, Newmarket Road, Bury St Edmunds, Suffolk IP33 3YB,
United Kingdom.
MUSIC SALES PTY LIMITED
Units 3-4, 17 Willfox Street, Condell Park, NSW 2200, Australia.

Order No. AM1006467
ISBN 978-1-78305-096-3
This book © Copyright 2013 Wise Publications, a division of Music Sales Limited.

Compiled and edited by Jenni Norey.
Cover designed by Michael Bell Design.
Printed in the EU.

www.musicsales.com

*SEE PAGE 136 FOR DETAILS OF
HOW TO ACCESS YOUR TRACKS

WISE PUBLICATIONS
part of The Music Sales Group
London / New York / Paris / Sydney / Copenhagen / Berlin / Madrid / Hong Kong / Tokyo

THE A TEAM ED SHEERAN 4
(Sheeran) Sony/ATV Music Publishing (UK) Limited

ALL ABOUT TONIGHT PIXIE LOTT 10
(Kidd/James/Ottoh) Universal/MCA Music Limited/BMG Rights Management (UK) Limited/Copyright Control

APOLOGIZE ONEREPUBLIC 7
(Tedder) Sony/ATV Music Publishing (UK) Limited

BABYLON DAVID GRAY 12
(Gray) Chrysalis Music Limited

BAD ROMANCE LADY GAGA 15
(Germanotta/RedOne) Sony/ATV Music Publishing (UK) Limited

BAKER STREET GERRY RAFFERTY 18
(Rafferty) Stage Three Music Publishing Limited

BEAUTIFUL CHRISTINA AGUILERA 22
(Perry) Sony/ATV Harmony UK

BEDSHAPED KEANE 28
(Rice-Oxley/Chaplin/Hughes/Sanger) Universal Music Publishing MGB Limited/Chrysalis Music Limited

BROKEN STRINGS JAMES MORRISON 30
(Morrison/Smith/Woodford) Chrysalis Music Limited/Sony/ATV Music Publishing (UK) Limited

BROWN EYED GIRL VAN MORRISON 25
(Morrison) Universal Music Publishing Limited

CHASING PAVEMENTS ADELE 32
(Adkins/White) Universal Music Publishing Limited

DOMINO JESSIE J 34
(Martin/Gottwald/Kelly/Cornish/Walter) Kobalt Music Publishing Limited/Warner/Chappell North America Limited/Sony/ATV Music Publishing (UK) Limited

DON'T LET THE SUN GO DOWN ON ME ELTON JOHN 37
(John/Taupin) Universal Music Publishing Limited

EVERY TEARDROP IS A WATERFALL COLDPLAY 40
(Castioni/Christensen/Lagonda/Wycombe/Berryman/Buckland/Champion/Martin/Eno/Allen/Anderson)
Universal Music Publishing MGB Limited/Opal Music/Universal Music Publishing International Limited/Warner/Chappell Overseas Holdings Limited

THE FEAR LILY ALLEN 46
(Allen/Kurstin) EMI Music Publishing Limited/Universal Music Publishing Limited

FORGET YOU CEE-LO GREEN 43
(Brown/Callaway/Levine/Lawrence/Hernandez) Chrysalis Music Limited/Warner/Chappell Music North America Limited/Bug Music (Windswept Account)/Bug Music Limited

GEORGIA ON MY MIND RAY CHARLES 48
(Gorrell/Carmichael) Campbell Connelly & Co. Limited

GLAD YOU CAME THE WANTED 50
(Hector/Mac/Drewett) Warner/Chappell Music Publishing Limited/BMG Rights Management (UK) Limited

GRENADE BRUNO MARS 52
(Lawrence/Hernandez/Brown/Levine/Kelly/Wyatt) Warner/Chappell North America Limited/Sony/ATV Music Publishing (UK) Limited/Bug Music (Windswept Account)/Bug Music Limited

HALLELUJAH ALEXANDRA BURKE 55
(Cohen) Sony/ATV Music Publishing (UK) Limited

HE AIN'T HEAVY, HE'S MY BROTHER THE HOLLIES 58
(Russell/Scott) Campbell Connelly & Co. Limited/Jenny Music Inc

HUMAN THE KILLERS 61
(Flowers/Keuning/Stoermer/Vannucci) Universal Music Publishing Limited

I STILL HAVEN'T FOUND WHAT I'M LOOKING FOR U2 64
(Mullen/Evans/Clayton/Hewson) Blue Mountain Music Limited

I WILL ALWAYS LOVE YOU WHITNEY HOUSTON 67
(Parton) Carlin Music Corporation

IF I WERE A BOY BEYONCÉ 70
(Gad/Carlson) BMG Rights Management (UK) Limited/Universal/MCA Music Limited

IT MUST BE LOVE MADNESS 73
(Siffre) Chrysalis Songs Limited

JAR OF HEARTS CHRISTINA PERRI 76
(Perri/Lawrence/Yeretsian) Warner/Chappell North America Limited/Wixen Music UK Limited/Fintage Publishing B.V.

JEALOUSY WILL YOUNG 79
(Young/Eliot/Stilwell) Sony/ATV Music Publishing (UK) Limited

LAST FRIDAY NIGHT KATY PERRY 82
(Martin/Gottwald/McKee/Perry) Kassner Associated Music Publishers Limited/Kobalt Music Publishing Limited/Warner/Chappell North America Limited

LEAN ON ME BILL WITHERS 84
(Withers) Universal/MCA Music Limited

LET IT BE THE BEATLES 86
(Lennon/McCartney) Sony/ATV Music Publishing (UK) Limited

LIVE AND LET DIE PAUL McCARTNEY 89
(McCartney/McCartney) MPL Communications Limited/EMI United Partnership Limited

LOVE GOES DOWN PLAN B 92
(Drew/Appapoulay/Cassell/Goss) Universal Music Publishing PGM Limited/Sony/ATV Music Publishing (UK) Limited

MAD WORLD TEARS FOR FEARS 94
(Orzabal) Chrysalis Music Limited

MAMMA MIA ABBA 96
(Andersson/Anderson/Ulvaeus) Bocu (ABBA) Music/Bocu Music Limited

PERFECT MOMENT MARTINE McCUTCHEON 102
(Marr/Page) Chrysalis Music Limited

RULE THE WORLD TAKE THAT 104
(Owen/Barlow/Orange/Donald) EMI Music Publishing Limited/Sony/ATV Music Publishing (UK) Limited/Universal Music Publishing Limited

RUN LEONA LEWIS 106
(Lightbody/Quinn/McClelland/Connolly/Archer) Universal Music Publishing Limited/Kobalt Music Publishing Limited

SOMEONE LIKE YOU ADELE 99
(Adkins/Wilson) Universal Music Publishing Limited/Chrysalis Music Limited

SOMETHIN' STUPID FRANK & NANCY SINATRA 108
(Parks) Montclare Music Company Limited

SUNDAY GIRL BLONDIE 111
(Stein) Chrysalis Music Limited

THANK YOU FOR THE MUSIC ABBA 114
(Andersson/Ulvaeus) Bocu (ABBA) Music/Bocu Music Limited

THRILLER MICHAEL JACKSON 120
(Temperton) Universal Music Publishing Limited

TRUE COLORS EVA CASSIDY 117
(Steinberg/Kelly) Sony/ATV Music Publishing (UK) Limited

VIVA LA VIDA COLDPLAY 122
(Berryman/Buckland/Champion/Martin) Universal Music Publishing MGB Limited

WHAT MAKES YOU BEAUTIFUL ONE DIRECTION 124
(Kotecha/Falk/Yacoub) Chrysalis Music Limited/EMI Music Publishing Limited/Kobalt Music Publishing Limited

WITH A LITTLE HELP FROM MY FRIENDS THE BEATLES 127
(Lennon/McCartney) Sony/ATV Music Publishing (UK) Limited

THE WORLD IS NOT ENOUGH GARBAGE 130
(Black/Arnold) Sony/ATV Music Publishing (UK) Limited

YELLOW COLDPLAY 132
(Berryman/Martin/Buckland/Champion) Universal Music Publishing MGB Limited

YOU RAISE ME UP WESTLIFE 134
(Graham/Løvland) Universal Music Publishing Limited/Peermusic (UK) Limited

The A Team

Words & Music by Ed Sheeran

Leisurely and simply ♩ = 85

D.S. al Coda

Coda

Apologize

Words & Music by Ryan Tedder

All About Tonight

Words & Music by Brian Kidd, Thomas James & Tebey Ottoh

Babylon

Words & Music by David Gray

Lightly, with a bounce ♩ = 112

Bad Romance

Words & Music by Stefani Germanotta & RedOne

With confidence ♩ = 119

(hi-hat cue)

D.S. al Coda

Coda

Baker Street

Words & Music by Gerry Rafferty

With a steady beat ♩ = 115

synth. cue

Beautiful

Words & Music by Linda Perry

Rock piano ballad, gradually building ♩ = 76

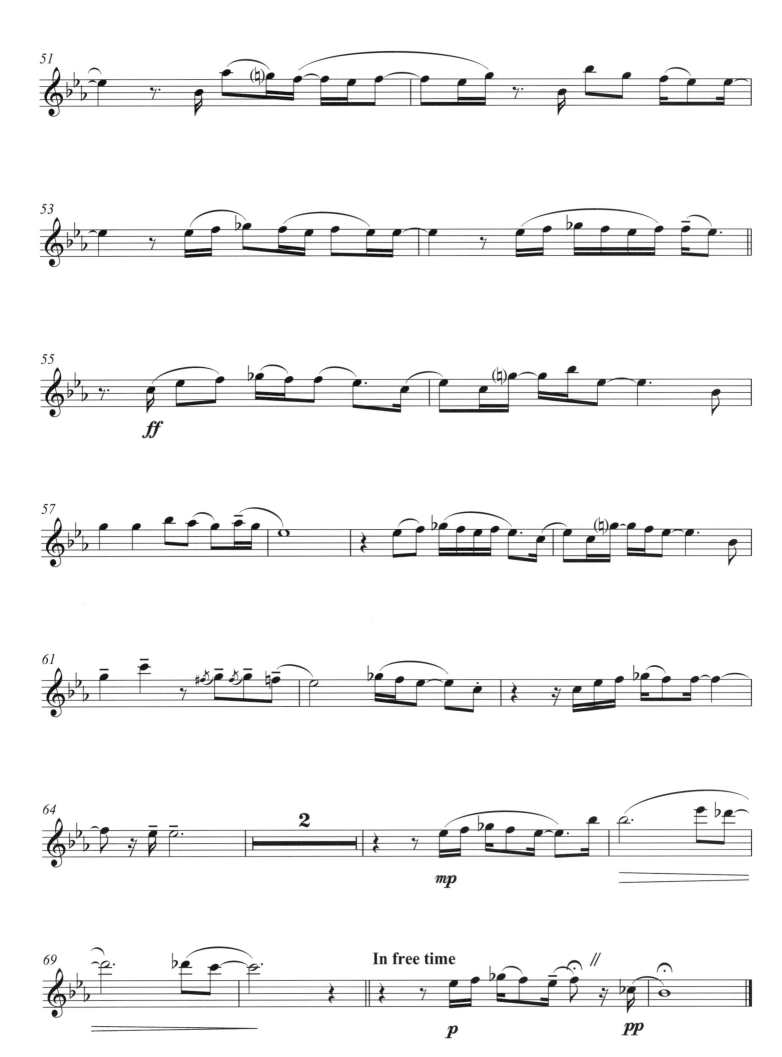

Brown Eyed Girl

Words & Music by Van Morrison

Bedshaped

Words & Music by Tim Rice-Oxley, Tom Chaplin,
Richard Hughes & James Sanger

Broken Strings

Words & Music by James Morrison, Fraser T. Smith
& Nina Woodford

Chasing Pavements

Words & Music by Adele Adkins & Eg White

Domino

Words & Music by Max Martin, Lukasz Gottwald,
Claude Kelly, Jessica Cornish & Henry Russell Walter

Lightly, with a bounce ♩ = 128

Don't Let The Sun Go Down On Me

Words & Music by Elton John & Bernie Taupin

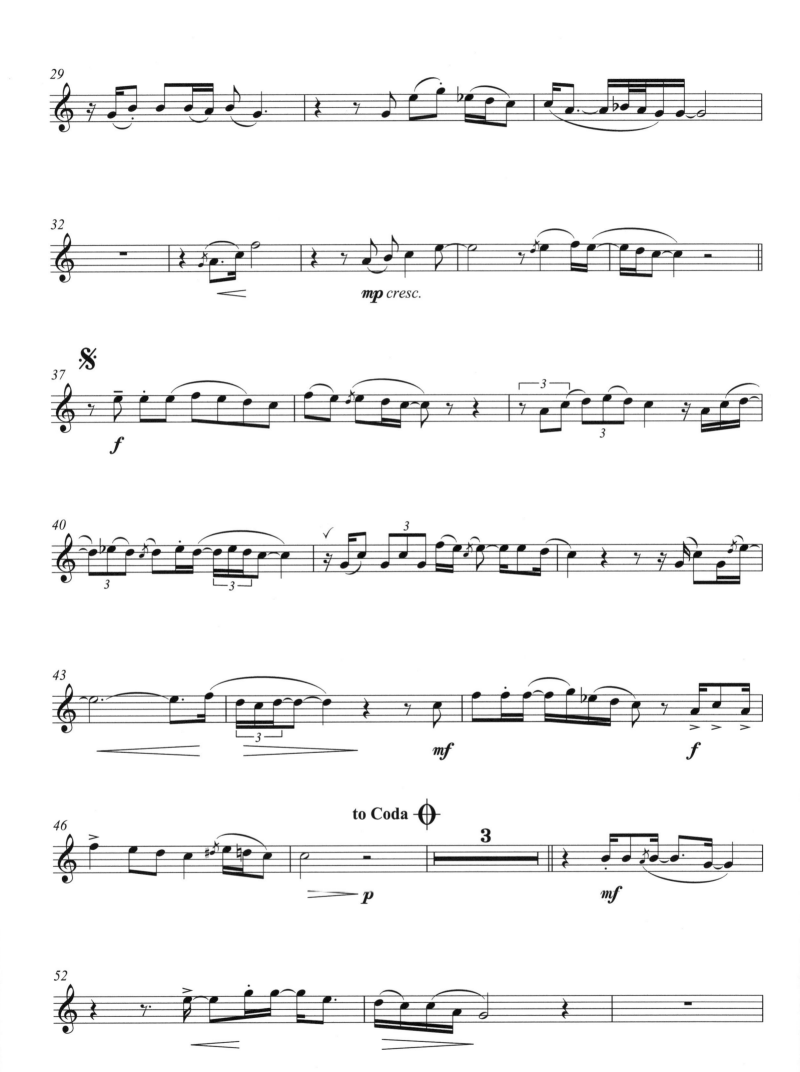

D.S. al Coda $\oplus$ **Coda**

Every Teardrop Is A Waterfall

Words & Music by Harry Castioni, Alex Christensen, B. Lagonda, Wycombe,
Guy Berryman, Jonathan Buckland, William Champion, Christopher Martin,
Brian Eno, Peter Allen and Adrienne Anderson

Forget You

Words & Music by Christopher Brown, Thomas Callaway,
Ari Levine, Philip Lawrence & Peter Hernandez

Energetically and rhythmically ♩ = 127

The Fear

Words & Music by Lily Allen & Greg Kurstin

Georgia On My Mind

Words by Stuart Gorrell
Music by Hoagy Carmichael

Relaxed swing, straight quavers ♩ = 60

violin cue

mp espressivo

Glad You Came

Words & Music by Wayne Hector, Steve Mac
& Ed Drewett

Sweetly ♩ = 112

(ride cymbal cue)   *mp*

Rhythmically ♩ = 127

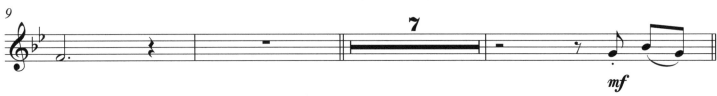

mf

50

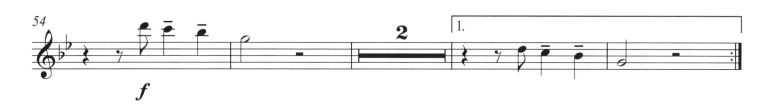

Grenade

Words & Music by Phillip Lawrence, Peter Hernandez,
Christopher Brown, Ari Levine, Claude Kelly & Andrew Wyatt

Hallelujah

Words & Music by Leonard Cohen

mf cantabile

f

mf espressivo

molto rall.

He Ain't Heavy, He's My Brother

Words & Music by Bob Russell & Robert William Scott

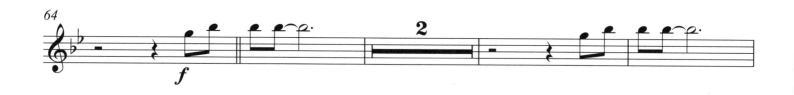

Human

Words by Brandon Flowers
Music by Brandon Flowers, Dave Keuning, Mark Stoermer & Ronnie Vannucci

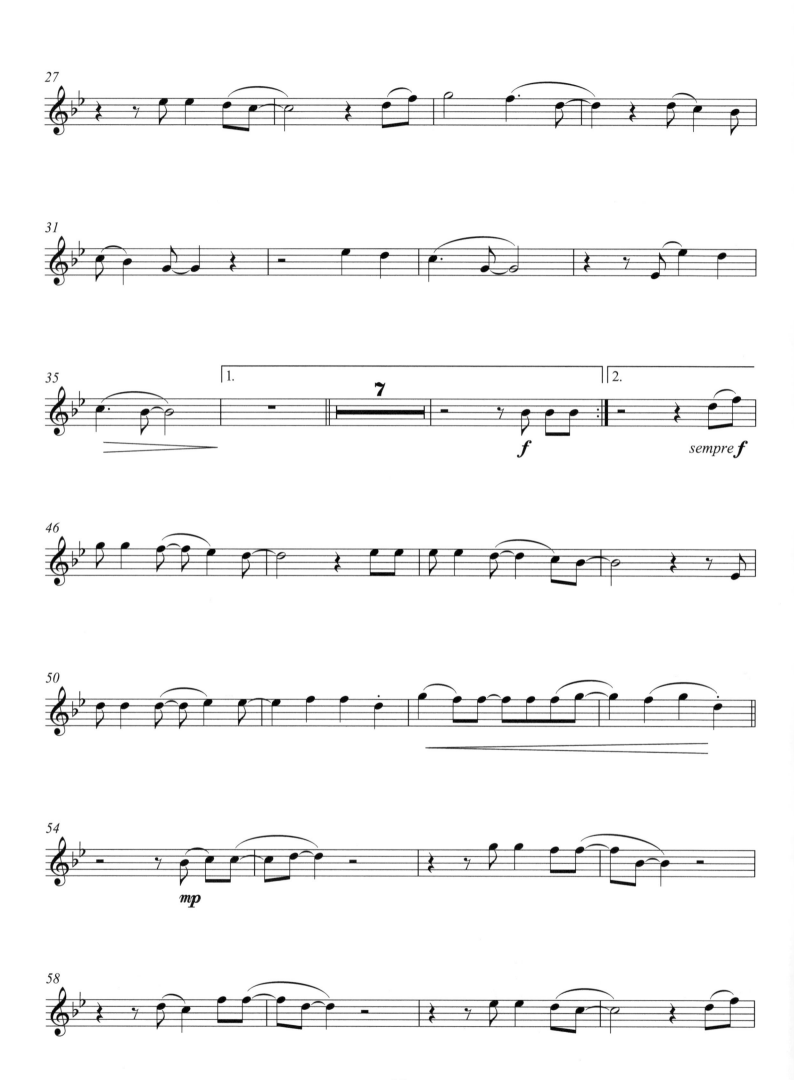

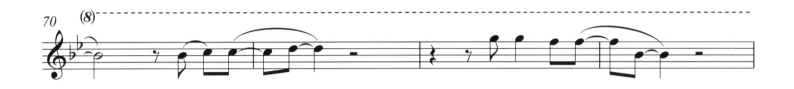

I Still Haven't Found What I'm Looking For

Words & Music by U2

I Will Always Love You

Words & Music by Dolly Parton

If I Were A Boy

Words & Music by Tobias Gad & Britney Carlson

Steadily and rhythmically ♩ = 90

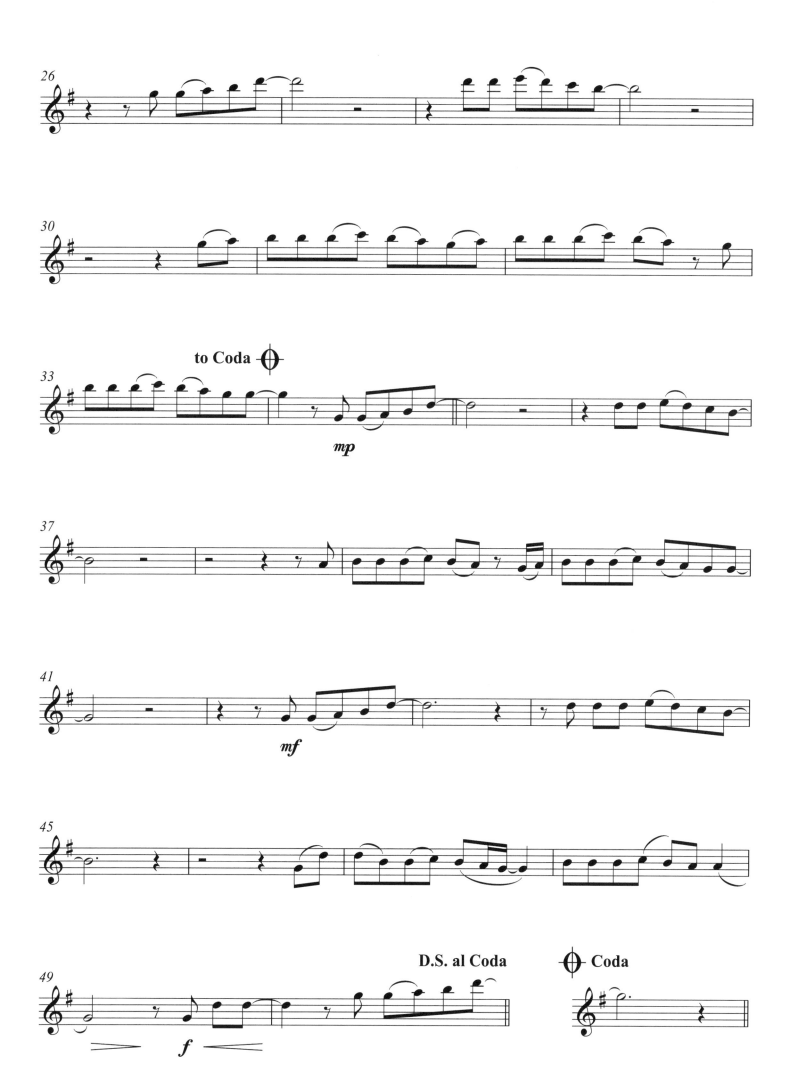

72

It Must Be Love

Words & Music by Labi Siffre

Jar Of Hearts

Words & Music by Christina Perri, Drew Lawrence
& Barrett Yeretsian

Jealousy

Words & Music by Will Young, James Eliot
& Jemima Stilwell

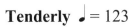

Last Friday Night

Words & Music by Max Martin, Lukasz Gottwald,
Bonnie McKee & Katy Perry

Lean On Me

Words & Music by Bill Withers

Let It Be

Words & Music by John Lennon & Paul McCartney

Live And Let Die

Words & Music by Paul & Linda McCartney

Reggae

Love Goes Down

Words & Music by Benjamin Drew, Eric Appapoulay,
Richard Cassell & Tom Goss

Mad World

Words & Music by Roland Orzabal

Mamma Mia

Words & Music by Benny Andersson, Stig Anderson
& Björn Ulvaeus

Moderately

Repeat and fade

Someone Like You

Words & Music by Adele Adkins & Daniel Wilson

Smoothly, with tenderness ♩ = 68

Perfect Moment

Words & Music by James Marr & Wendy Page

Rule The World

Words & Music by Mark Owen, Gary Barlow,
Jason Orange & Howard Donald

Run

Words & Music by Gary Lightbody, Jonathan Quinn,
Mark McClelland, Nathan Connolly & Iain Archer

Somethin' Stupid

Words & Music by C. Carson Parks

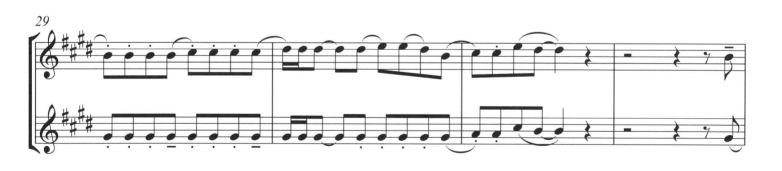

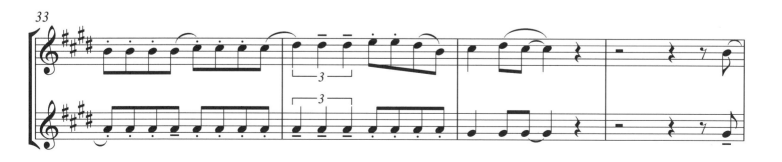

Repeat to fade

110

Sunday Girl

Words & Music by Chris Stein

With a bounce ♩ = 146

Repeat and fade

113

Thank You For The Music

Words & Music by Benny Andersson & Björn Ulvaeus

poco rall. slower

True Colors

Words & Music by Billy Steinberg & Tom Kelly

(guitar solo)

molto rit.

Thriller

Words & Music by Rod Temperton

Viva La Vida

Words & Music by Guy Berryman, Jon Buckland,
Will Champion & Chris Martin

What Makes You Beautiful

Words & Music by Savan Kotecha, Carl Falk
& Rami Yacoub

Steadily and smoothly ♩ = 125

With A Little Help From My Friends

Words & Music by John Lennon & Paul McCartney

The World Is Not Enough

Words by Don Black
Music by David Arnold

Powerfully, with a steady beat ♩ = 86

Yellow

Words & Music by Guy Berryman, Chris Martin,
Jon Buckland & Will Champion

You Raise Me Up

Words & Music by Brendan Graham & Rolf Løvland

123456789

HOW TO DOWNLOAD YOUR MUSIC TRACKS

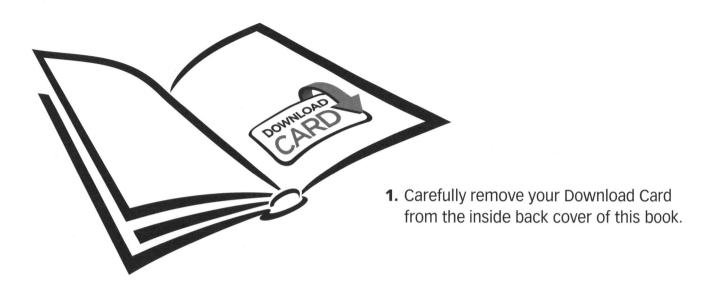

1. Carefully remove your Download Card from the inside back cover of this book.

2. On the back of the card is your unique access code. Enter this at www.musicsalesdownloads.com

TO REDEEM THIS CARD VISIT
www.musicsalesdownloads.com

ENTER ACCESS CODE:

XXXXXXXXXX

Download Cards are powered by Dropcards.
User must accept terms at dropcards.com/terms
which are adopted by The Music Sales Group.
Not reedemable for cash. Void where prohibited or restricted by law.

DCARD1006478

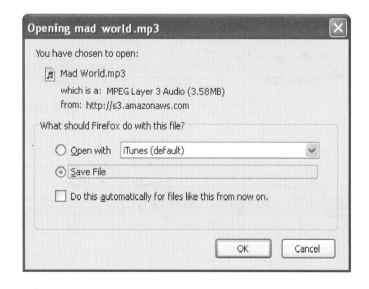

3. Follow the instructions to save your files to your computer*. That's it!

*Appearance of download manager will vary depending upon operating system and web browser.
In case of difficulty when downloading files, please contact dropcards.com/help
Card missing? Please contact music@musicsales.co.uk